Specimen Sight-Reading Tests

Piano

by Alan Ridout

Grade 7

The Associated Board of
the Royal Schools of Music

Flowing

AB 2401

Adagio e mesto (Homage to Schnittke)

Pesante (Homage to Hindemith)

Adagio (Homage to Albinoni)

Allegretto (Homage to Virgil Thomson)

AB 2401

8

Moderato

Vivace (Homage to Milhaud)

Moderato (Homage to Steve Reich)

10

p staccato

mp

p

11 Scherzoso

12

Allegretto (Homage to William Mathias)

13

AB 2401

Lento (Homage to Mozart)

Andantino (Homage to Skryabin)

mf espress.

15

Printed in England by Caligraving Limited Thetford Norfolk

AB 2401

10:00